Library of Congress Control Number: 2015936071

ISBN 978-93-89823-97-4

First edition, March 2016
This edition: August 2022
Edited by Cassandra Pelham
Book Design by Kazu Kibuishi and Phil Falco
Creative Director: David Saylor

Printed in India

AMULET

KAZU KIBUISHI

BOOK SEVEN
FIRELIGHT

AN IMPRINT OF
SCHOLASTIC

4

MORNING, MISS EMILY!

GOOD MORNING, RICO.

I HAVE NEVER HEARD OF ALGOS ISLAND, CHIEF.

SO I'M NOT SURPRISED WE CAN'T FIND IT ON ANY MAP.

WE'RE NOT FOLLOWING A MAP.

EMILY IS GUIDED BY HER STONE.

WHAT'S ON THIS ISLAND, ANYWAY?

WHATEVER IT IS, I GET HALF OF IT!

IT'S NOT TREASURE, ENZO.

WE'RE GOING THERE TO FIND MEMORIES.

MEMORIES?!!

YOU'RE KIDDING, RIGHT?!

THEY'RE THE REASON MAX WANTS ME TO GO THERE.

TO SEE WHAT HAPPENED WHEN I WAS YOUNG.

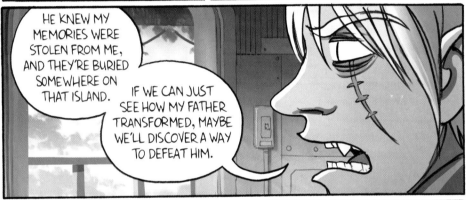

HE KNEW MY MEMORIES WERE STOLEN FROM ME, AND THEY'RE BURIED SOMEWHERE ON THAT ISLAND.

IF WE CAN JUST SEE HOW MY FATHER TRANSFORMED, MAYBE WE'LL DISCOVER A WAY TO DEFEAT HIM.

IT'S GOING TO TAKE A WHOLE LOT MORE THAN MEMORIES TO DEFEAT THE ELF KING!

THIS SOUNDS LIKE ANOTHER TRAP TO ME!

YOU GUYS ARE TOO GULLIBLE!

YOU'D MAKE TERRIBLE PIRATES!

ENZO!

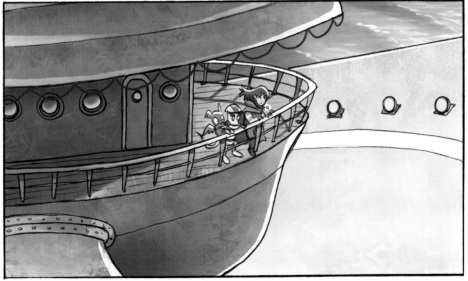

EVEN IF WE FIND OUT HOW THE ELF KING CAME TO BE, WHAT GOOD WILL IT DO?

WE STILL HAVE TO FIGHT HIM.

TRELLIS'S STOLEN MEMORIES CAN SHOW US WHAT HAPPENED TO THE ELF KING.

IF WE STUDY HOW THE ENEMY THINKS, WE CAN USE IT TO OUR ADVANTAGE.

AND WHAT MAKES YOU BELIEVE THAT EVERY TIME YOU ENTER THE VOID, HE IS NOT DOING THE SAME WITH YOU?

BE CAREFUL WHO YOU TRUST, CHIEF.

NOT EVERYONE YOU BELIEVE IS AN ALLY HAS YOUR BEST INTERESTS AT HEART.

I DON'T THINK ANYONE HAS BEEN HERE FOR A LONG TIME, VIGO.

THE ORIGINAL OCCUPANTS MAY HAVE VACATED LONG AGO,

BUT NEW CREATURES MAY HAVE TAKEN UP RESIDENCE HERE.

SO STAY ALERT.

GET YOUR HOT SOUP HERE!

YOU POOR ANGELS LOOK SO HUNGRY.

HERE--

THIS ONE'S ON ME.

ARE THEY GHOSTS?

MEMORIES.

THE HISTORY OF THIS STATION IS BEING REVEALED TO US.

AND IT APPEARS THE ATTACKERS WERE NOT PIRATES, BUT STONE-KEEPERS.

IF THIS STATION WAS ATTACKED BY STONEKEEPERS, TWO QUESTIONS REMAIN--

WHO WOULD DO SUCH A THING AND WHY WOULD THEY DO IT?

MAX?

MAX WOULD NEVER ORDER AN ATTACK LIKE THIS. NOT AGAINST CIVILIANS WITHOUT TIES TO CIELIS.

SOMETHING ODD HAPPENED HERE.

MAX WANTED US TO KNOW ABOUT IT.

VIGO, WE'RE NOT IN THE VOID, OR IN A STRUCTURE BUILT BY STONEKEEPERS.

THESE WALLS SHOULD NOT CONTAIN ANY MAGIC,

SO WHY DO WE SEE ALL OF THIS?

22

I COULD TELL YOU BEING NEAR ALGOS ISLAND HAS SOMETHING TO DO WITH IT--

BUT THE TRUTH IS THAT I DON'T KNOW.

VIGO, THERE'S A REASON WE DIDN'T SEE ALGOS ISLAND ON THE MAP.

IT WAS NEVER AN ACTUAL ISLAND.

WE BETTER GO BACK AND TELL THE OTHERS TO JOIN US.

WE'RE ALREADY HERE.

IT'S REALLY COMING DOWN NOW, ENZO.

I WISH WE HAD A WAY TO LET THE OTHERS KNOW.

WE'RE FUELED UP NOW.

IF THEY DON'T RETURN SOON, WE HAVE TO GO.

WE CAN'T JUST LEAVE THEM BEHIND!!!

WHEN THAT STORM HITS, WE HAVE TO BE OUT OF HERE.

OR ELSE WE LOSE THE LUNA MOTH AND WE'LL ALL BE TRAPPED.

WITH A FULL TANK OF GAS, WE CAN FLY OUT AND GET BACK HERE AFTER THE STORM PASSES.

THEY JUST HAVE TO TRUST US.

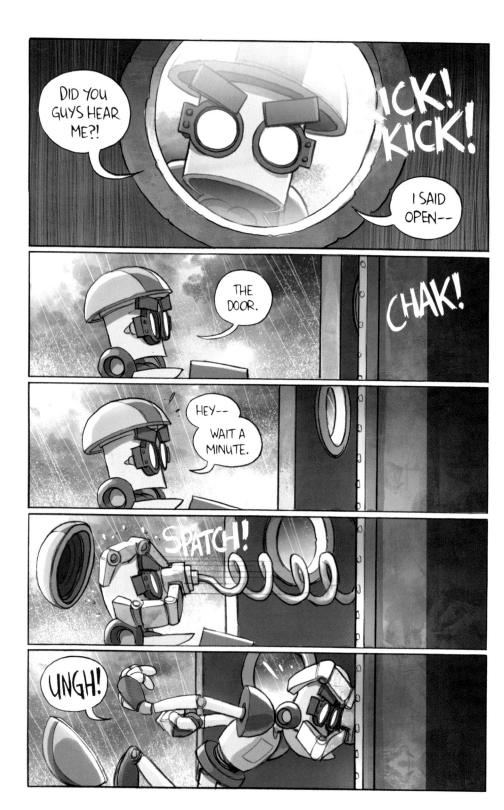

26

ENZO!
WE NEED TO GIVE THEM MORE TIME!

I'M GOING TO GET THE ENGINE READY!

HEY KID, WHERE'S THE BUCKET OF BOLTS?

CHEE!

29

35

YOU ARE FOOLISH TO TRUST THE STONEKEEPERS.

ESPECIALLY THE GIRL. SHE WILL SPELL YOUR DOOM.

I DIDN'T ASK FOR ADVICE, PAL.

LOOK WHAT WE FOUND! HE WAS CAUGHT SNEAKING AROUND THE SHIP.

GABILAN?

WHAT HAPPENED TO HIM?

THIS IS HOW WE FOUND HIM, BANDAGES AND ALL.

DO YOU KNOW WHY WE'RE HERE?

37

TRELLIS AND I WILL ACCOMPANY YOU ON THE JOURNEY.

EMILY, YOU MUST TAKE ME WITH YOU.

THE COUNCIL NEEDS YOU MORE THAN ME, VIGO.

YOUR HISTORY WITH MAX ALSO MAKES YOU TOO VULNERABLE.

IT WILL PUT US ALL AT RISK.

WHAT MAKES YOU LESS VULNERABLE?

I'M THE ONLY ONE THAT'S NOT FROM THIS WORLD. I DON'T HAVE A HISTORY HERE.

NOW TAKE US TO THE DOCK.

NO ONE TRAINS TO BECOME A STONEKEEPER. YOU MUST HAVE BEEN CHOSEN, LIKE YOUR ANCESTORS BEFORE YOU.

NO. THIS WAS MY CHOICE.

THEN YOUR PROBLEMS ARE WORSE THAN I IMAGINED.

WATCH YOUR HEAD.

THIS SUBMARINE WAS ASSEMBLED IN LUCIEN. GREAT CONSTRUCTION.

IT IS WELL-SUITED FOR THESE EXPEDITIONS.

MY TRIPS TO THE CORTEX HAVE BEEN AT THE REQUEST OF THOSE WHO WANTED MEMORIES ERASED AND FORGOTTEN.

I HAVE NEVER TRAVELED THERE TO HELP SOMEONE REMEMBER.

THESE MEMORIES ARE THE KIND YOU WANT TO FORGET.

THAT'S NOT FOR YOU TO DECIDE.

43

SHE'S A SMART KID, VIGO. SHE'LL BE ALL RIGHT.

I KNOW.

BUT I WAS A FATHER ONCE, AND THAT PART OF ME WILL NEVER GO AWAY.

I'M A COMPUTER, SO I HAVE NO IDEA WHAT YOU'RE TALKING ABOUT.

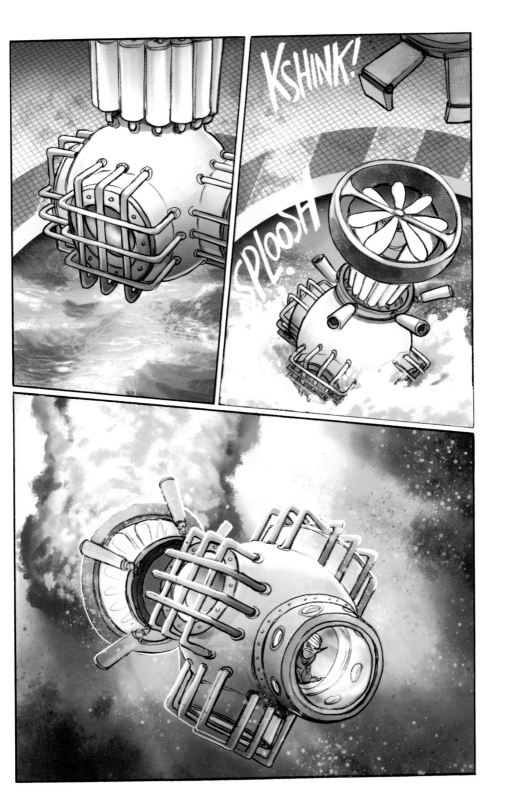

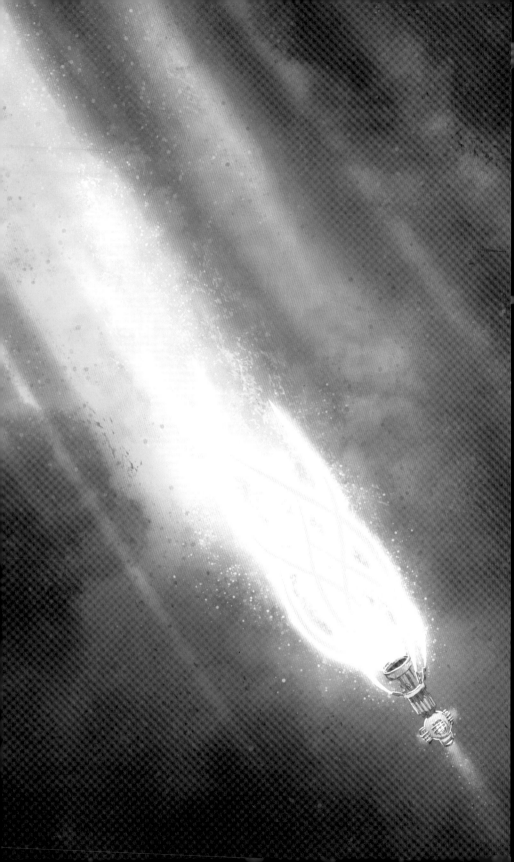

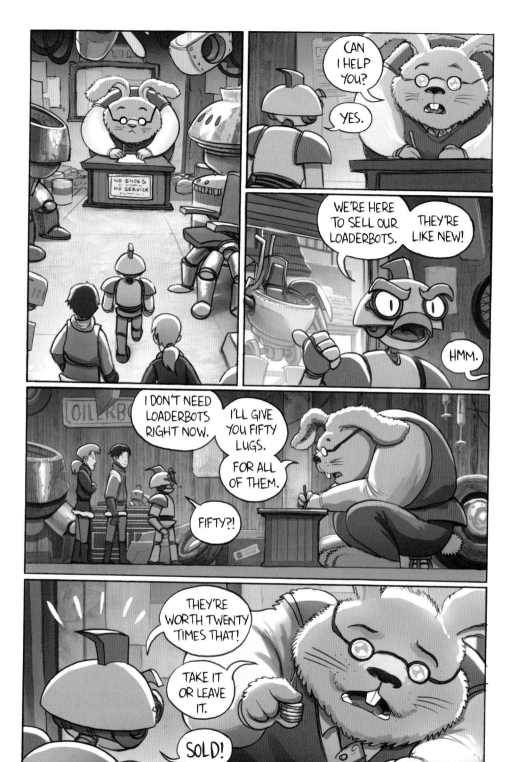

FIFTY LUGS ISN'T GOING TO BUY EVEN ONE TICKET.

WE'LL JUST EXPLAIN OUR SITUATION.

THEY MUST KNOW OF OUR MISSION AND ITS SIGNIFICANCE!

TICKETS

NEXT IN LINE, PLEASE.

AHEM.

I'M GENERAL PIL, FROM THE CITY OF LUCIEN. WE NEED TO BE GIVEN PASSAGE TO FRONTERA.

OH DEAR.

WE CAN'T JUST GIVE TICKETS AWAY.

PLEASE, MA'AM—

THIS IS EXTREMELY URGENT.

WELL—

HOW ABOUT IF I FIND YOU JOBS ON ONE OF THE SHIPS?

YES, WE CAN WORK!

IF YOU'RE WILLING TO WAIT TABLES, THEN I HAVE SOME OPENINGS FOR YOU.

MA'AM, I AM A MASTER CHEF! I ONLY WORK IN THE KITCHEN!

WELL, YOU'RE IN LUCK.

THERE IS ALSO A JOB OPENING IN THE KITCHEN. THEY NEED A SOUS CHEF.

SOLD!

GENERAL, WE DON'T HAVE TIME TO WORK IN A RESTAURANT.

COMMANDER NAVIN, WE'RE ONLY GOING TO PRETEND WE'RE WORKING ON THE SHIP!

THE MOMENT WE ARRIVE IN FRONTERA, WE'RE OUT OF THERE!

55

ISN'T THAT DISHONEST?

MISS HUNTER --

PEOPLE DO IT ALL THE TIME!

SAYING THEY WILL DO SOMETHING AND THEY JUST DON'T DO IT.

IT'S NORMAL!

THAT'S NOT HOW WE DO THINGS.

WE TELL THEM THE TRUTH.

THIS MIGHT JEOPARDIZE THE ENTIRE MISSION, COMMANDER.

WE MAY NOT GET PERMISSION TO BOARD!

SO BE IT.

BUT I WON'T LIE TO THEM.

GOOD GRIEF.

I ASKED FOR EXPERIENCED KITCHEN STAFF AND THEY SEND ME KIDS!

THIS IS A JOKE, RIGHT?!

ARE ALL THOSE PEOPLE LINING UP FOR DINNER?

YOU'RE NOT EVEN OPEN YET!

THAT'S RIGHT.

WE DON'T TAKE RESERVATIONS, SO THEY LINE UP EARLY IF THEY WANT A TABLE.

PEOPLE TRAVEL FROM ALL OVER THE WORLD FOR A MEAL HERE.

THAT'S AMAZING.

IT WASN'T ALWAYS LIKE THIS.

WE HAVE MANY CUSTOMERS NOW, BUT IT TOOK YEARS FOR THIS RESTAURANT TO GET TO A POINT WHERE I COULD SAY IT WAS WORKING OUT ALL RIGHT.

HOW LONG AGO DID YOU START WORKING AS A CHEF?

I GRADUATED FROM CULINARY SCHOOL ALMOST TWENTY YEARS AGO.

THAT'S WHEN I DECIDED TO OPEN A RESTAURANT.

IS THIS THAT RESTAURANT?

NO.

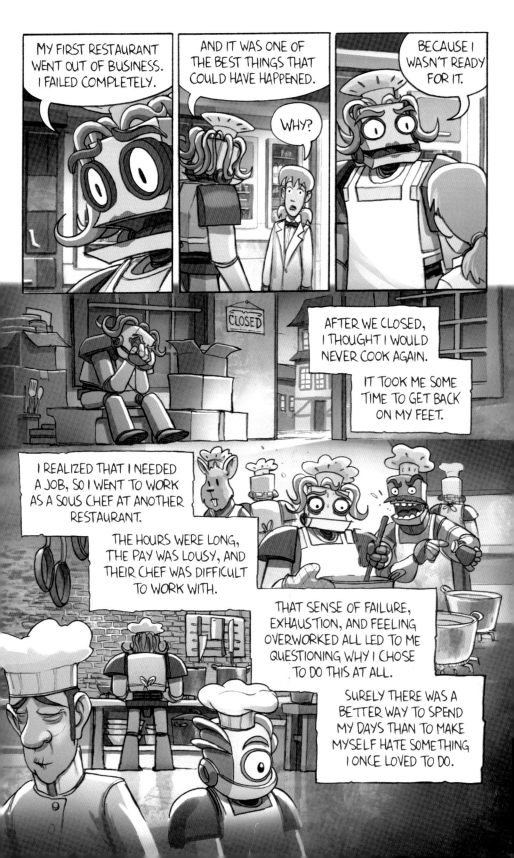

WHILE I WORKED I SPENT A LOT OF TIME THINKING ABOUT WHY I DECIDED TO BE A CHEF.

WHY DID I DEDICATE SO MUCH OF MY LIFE TO THIS?

I USED TO THINK IT WAS FOR SUCCESS OR RECOGNITION, BUT I DIDN'T CARE ABOUT THOSE THINGS ANYMORE.

AND THEN ONE EVENING, WHILE PREPARING FOR A BUSY NIGHT AT WORK, I REALIZED WHAT IT WAS AND ALWAYS HAS BEEN.

IT'S FAMILY.

FAMILY?

THE REASON I'VE BEEN DOING THIS ALL ALONG.

TO NURTURE, TO CONNECT, TO FEED FAMILIES.

EVEN INSIDE THE KITCHEN.

AS A CHILD, I BEGAN COOKING TO FEED MY BROTHERS AND SISTERS.

EVEN MY PARENTS AND GRANDPARENTS.

AND I'VE BEEN DOING IT EVER SINCE.

64

WHEN I OPENED THIS PLACE, I WANTED TO RE-CREATE THE FEELING I HAD WHEN I COOKED FOR MY FAMILY.

NO MATTER WHO YOU ARE OR WHERE YOU'RE FROM, DINING AT SUZY'S SHOULD MAKE YOU FEEL AT HOME.

THE WORLD IS A CRAZY PLACE, GETTING WEIRDER BY THE DAY--

SO IT'S NICE FOR PEOPLE TO HAVE AT LEAST ONE PLACE TO GO THAT THEY CAN CALL HOME.

REMEMBER THAT TONIGHT, OKAY?

REMEMBER WHAT SUZY SAID.

REMEMBER WHAT SUZY SAID.

MAKE EVERYONE FEEL LIKE THEY'RE AT HOME.

HEY.

YOU ARE IN TERRIBLE DANGER HERE.

I DON'T KNOW WHO YOU THINK I AM, BUT--

CUT OUT THE BAD ACTING, COMMANDER.

I KNOW WHO YOU ARE.

AND I DON'T THINK I'M THE ONLY ONE HERE WHO DOES.

WANTED

WE NEED TO TALK.

MEET ME IN THE KITCHEN.

PSST! OVER HERE!

I RECOGNIZED SOME BOUNTY HUNTERS IN THE CROWD WHO YOU WILL WANT TO AVOID IF AT ALL POSSIBLE.

THERE ARE TWO IN PARTICULAR WHO MAY CAUSE SOME TROUBLE.

GATHER EVERYONE AND BE READY TO GO AT THE REAR CABIN EXIT.

I'LL SLOW DOWN OUR BOUNTY HUNTER FRIENDS.

GRAVIS, LOOK.

IS THAT WHO I THINK IT IS?

TO THE KITCHEN, QUICKLY.

MAKE SURE TO LET THE RESISTANCE KNOW THEY GET A DISCOUNT FOR DINING HERE!

I WILL!

HEY, DON'T FORGET TO VISIT US.

AS A CUSTOMER NEXT TIME.

I WON'T FORGET FAMILY.

THANKS, SUZY.

I'M SORRY I DIDN'T INTRODUCE MYSELF BACK THERE.

MY NAME IS LONI, AND THIS IS MY BROTHER, RONI.

WELCOME ABOARD!

THAT AIRSHIP WAS ON ITS WAY TO FRONTERA.

WHAT PROMPTED YOU TO GO THERE?

WE FIGURED IT WAS OUR BEST CHANCE OF ENTERING VALCOR.

AND HOW DID YOU PLAN TO GET INTO VALCOR ONCE YOU GOT THERE?

IMPROVISE.

HAH! YOU'RE CRAZY!

DO YOU KNOW WHAT HAPPENS WHEN STONEKEEPERS LOSE CONTROL OF THEIR POWERS?

YES.

I HAVE WITNESSED IT HAPPEN.

HAVE YOU?

MANY YEARS AGO.

I WAS MUCH YOUNGER, WORKING ON THE FAMILY FARM, WHERE WE BRED STORMBIRDS FOR THE ELF ARMY'S WAR EFFORTS.

FOUR GENERATIONS OF MY FAMILY WERE RAISED ON THE FARM, AND WE WERE ALL EXPERTS AT BREEDING AND TRAINING THE BIRDS.

WE UNDERSTOOD THEY WERE BEING USED AS WEAPONS OF WAR, BUT THEY ALSO RARELY SAW COMBAT.

AND NEITHER DID WE.

UNTIL THE NIGHT THE WAR ARRIVED AT OUR DOORSTEP.

THOOM!

POOMF!

FROM THAT DAY FORWARD, I KNEW THE ELF KING WOULD CAST ME AS A FUGITIVE FOR FAILING HIM.

I KNEW HE WOULD HUNT ME DOWN.

I ALSO KNEW HE WOULD WANT THE MEMORIES I STOLE FROM HIS ENEMIES.

SO I HID THEM BENEATH THE SEA.

THESE CAVERNS WERE DISCOVERED BY THE CIELIS GUARD LONG AGO.

THEY FOUND A SIGNAL SUGGESTING A SECOND MOTHER STONE WAS BURIED DEEP WITHIN THE CAVERNS, SO THEY WENT TO GREAT LENGTHS TO FIND IT.

NO. THEY DISCOVERED SOMETHING ELSE.

DID THEY FIND IT?

WHAT PRODUCED THE SIGNAL WAS NOT A MOTHER STONE.

INSTEAD, THEY FOUND A STRUCTURE THAT LOOKED LIKE A GIANT SPACESHIP.

BUT THE WAR BROKE OUT AND ALL OF THEIR MISSIONS TO RESEARCH THE SHIP WERE DITCHED IN FAVOR OF THE WAR EFFORT.

THAT'S WHEN I DISCOVERED IT, LEFT ABANDONED.

I FOUND IT BY WAY OF ALGOS ISLAND, WHEN PEOPLE STILL LIVED THERE PEACEFULLY.

SO WHAT HAPPENED ON THE ISLAND?

SOME OF ALGOS ISLAND'S CITIZENS SEEMED FRIGHTENED OF US WHEN WE APPROACHED.

WHY?

WHY DO YOU THINK?

BECAUSE A STONEKEEPER KILLED THEM ALL.

WAS IT MAX?

NO.

IT WAS A MUCH YOUNGER STONEKEEPER WHO LOST CONTROL OF HIS POWERS.

AND WHEN HE LOST CONTROL, HE TURNED INTO A MONSTER.

HE WAS THE STONEKEEPER WHO ATTACKED YOUR FAMILY.

YES.

I SPENT YEARS STUDYING HIS LIFE, TRYING TO FIGURE OUT WHY IT HAPPENED.

I WANTED TO KNOW HOW SUCH MONSTERS WERE CREATED.

I WANTED TO KNOW, SO I COULD STOP THEM.

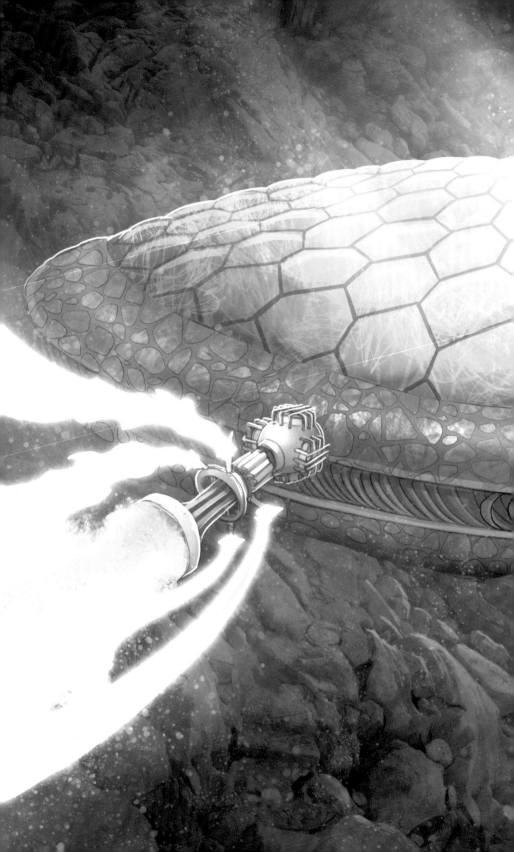

THAT SHIP IS THE SIZE OF A CITY.

I THINK IT IS THE SEED FOR A CITY.

EVERYTHING A NEW CITY NEEDS TO BEGIN IS CONTAINED IN THAT DOME.

AND THIS IS WHERE YOU'VE BEEN STORING MEMORIES?

YES. IT HAS PROVEN TO BE AN IDEAL LOCATION.

THE SHIP WAS ABANDONED IN A PLACE FEW DARED TO LOOK. SO I HAVE BEEN ABLE TO USE IT FOR MY OWN RESEARCH--

UTILIZING THE ADVANCED TECHNOLOGY FOR MY OWN NEEDS.

CAN WE BREATHE OUT THERE?

YES.

THE AIR DOWN HERE IS BETTER THAN ON THE SURFACE.

THE WATER IS BEING SUSPENDED IN THE AIR LIKE A WALL.

HOW IS THAT POSSIBLE?

THE SHIP CAN ALTER THE MOLECULAR STRUCTURE OF ITS ENVIRONMENT--

PROVIDING US WITH THE CONDITIONS WE NEED TO SURVIVE, BASED ON A PROFILE OF US.

SOMEDAY WE WILL UNDERSTAND HOW ALL OF IT WORKS.

UNTIL THEN, THEIR TECHNOLOGY IS STILL JUST MAGIC TO YOU AND ME.

DOWN THIS HALL WE WILL ENTER THE FIELD OF MEMORIES.

WHEN YOU ENTER, I NEED YOU TO REMEMBER ONE RULE--

YOU WILL BE SURROUNDED BY MEMORY CUBES THAT I'VE COLLECTED OVER THE YEARS.

DO NOT TOUCH ANY- THING.

THE NEXUS ALLOWS ME TO VIEW THE CONTENTS OF THE STORED MEMORIES, BUT ONLY STONEKEEPERS CAN ENTER THEM.

YOU CAN INTERACT AND EVEN ALTER THE MEMORIES.

A MOST ENVIABLE GIFT.

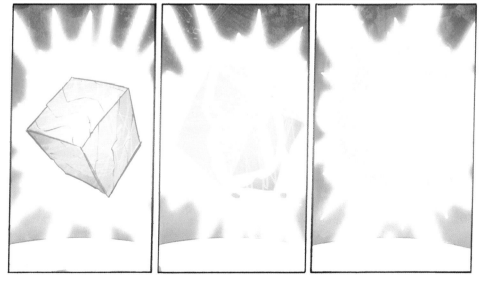

YOU FOLLOWED ME TO THE BOTTOM OF THE OCEAN.

I THINK IT'S TOO LATE TO LOSE YOUR TRUST IN ME.

BESIDES--

YOU'LL NEED SOMEONE TO STAY HERE AND HELP BUY YOU TIME.

I ALSO HAVE TO TRUST YOU WON'T LEAVE ME HERE.

YOU HAVE MY WORD.

STAY CLOSE, EMILY.

111

THEIR PLANET IS DYING. ISN'T IT, UNCLE VIRGIL?

YES.

THE PLANET'S RESOURCES HAVE BEEN EXHAUSTED.

ZOOM IN ON THE NORTHERN HEMISPHERE.

THEY'RE LEAVING.

THEY LEFT MANY YEARS AGO. THIS IS AN OLD SIGNAL.

WHAT'S INSIDE THOSE SHIPS?

APPROXIMATELY ONE HUNDRED SEVENTY THOUSAND LIFE-FORMS. MOST OF THEM ARE IN HYPERSLEEP, TENDED TO BY OTHER PARASITIC ORGANISMS ON BOARD.

THERE ARE AN ESTIMATED TWENTY THOUSAND OF THESE PARASITES.

SHOW THEM TO ME.

THEY ARE MADE MOSTLY OF GAS AND REQUIRE HOSTS TO SURVIVE.

SHADOWS.

IS MY FATHER ONE OF THEM?

YES.

TRELLIS.

I WARNED YOU NOT TO BE IN HERE.

I WARNED YOU IN ORDER TO PROTECT YOU.

NOW I SEE THAT I CAN NO LONGER TRUST YOU.

NOT WITHOUT A LITTLE--

ADJUSTMENT.

HE WOULD HAVE SEEN PAST YOUR LIES.

YOU CAN'T KEEP HIM FROM THE TRUTH!

HE WILL LEARN WHAT HE NEEDS TO PREPARE FOR ASCENSION TO THE THRONE.

LIAR!

YOU ARE PREPARING TO GET RID OF HIM, TO BREAK APART THIS KINGDOM!

I'VE SEEN ENOUGH.

YOUR FATHER IS NOT THE ONE WE NEED TO WORRY ABOUT.

THE VOICE MUST BE CONTROLLING THE KING THE WAY HE TRIES TO TAKE CONTROL OF US.

HE'S BEEN TRYING TO USE US TO PREPARE FOR THE ARRIVAL OF THOSE SHIPS.

TRYING?

HOW DO WE KNOW HE IS NOT SUCCEEDING?

EVERYTHING WE HAVE DONE SEEMS TO WORK TO HIS ADVANTAGE.

AT WHAT POINT HAVE WE EVER BEEN IN CONTROL?

143

144

145

147

FASH!!

164

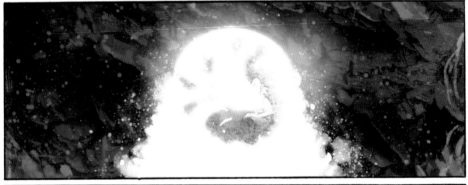

176

FRONTERA'S AIRPORT WAS DESTROYED BY CHRONOS THE MOUNTAIN GIANT.

IT WAS NEVER REPAIRED AND THIS CITY HASN'T RECOVERED SINCE THE ATTACK.

MOST OF FRONTERA'S CITIZENS LEFT. VERY FEW STAYED BEHIND.

IT PROVIDED US WITH A PERFECT OPPORTUNITY.

AFTER THE CITIZENS BEGAN TO LEAVE, WE SLOWLY STARTED TO MOVE IN HERE.

MOST OF THE UNDERGROUND INFRASTRUCTURE REMAINED INTACT.

AND THE CITY IS RELATIVELY NEW.

IT TURNED OUT TO BE A PERFECT CANDIDATE FOR OUR NEW HOME BASE.

HOME BASE FOR WHO?

FOR THE NEW RESISTANCE.

WELCOME HOME, COMMANDER.

OF COURSE, NOTHING'S SAFE ON ALLEDIAN SOIL RIGHT NOW, SO WE DO HAVE ANOTHER BASE, QUITE HIGH ABOVE.

HEY--

SOMETHING'S HEADING THIS WAY.

THOOM! THOOM!

IT'S A BEAST!

NO. IT'S OUR WELCOMING COMMITTEE.

HELLO, UNCLE TEX!

UNCLE TEX?

PSH!!

185

WAIT-- DOES HE KNOW WHY HE'S HERE?

I ASSUMED RIVA LET HIM KNOW.

GOODNESS, YOU MUST THINK WE'RE RUNNING A TWO-BIT OPERATION!

WE'LL FIX THAT, BOSS!

JUST FOLLOW ME!

WHEN THE KING WENT NUTTY, WE HAD TO TAKE THE SPACE PROGRAM UNDERGROUND. OUR RESEARCH UNCOVERED HOW THE SHADOWS TOOK CONTROL OF THE LAND.

WHEN OLD PLATE FACE SAW WHAT WE WERE UP TO--

HE TRIED TO DISMANTLE THE ENTIRE PROGRAM.

AND WHAT WERE YOU UP TO?

WE WERE PREPARING TO FIGHT BACK.

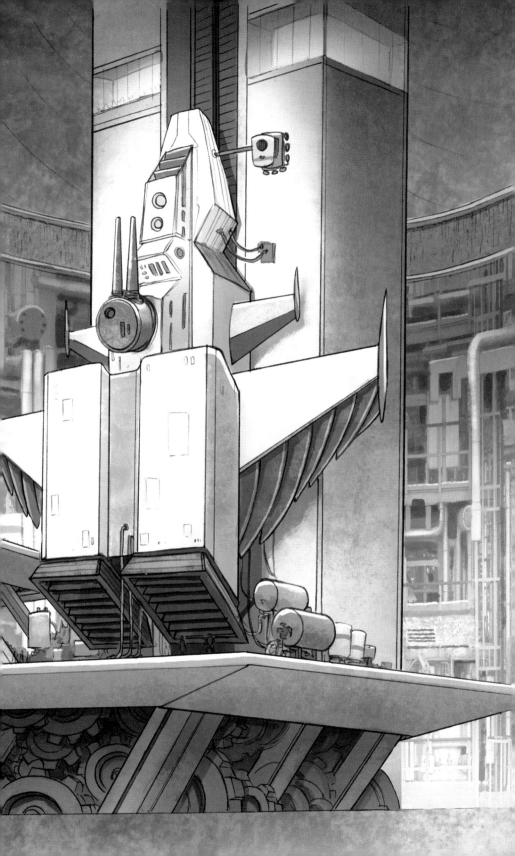

IT LOOKS LIKE THIS IS WHERE WE PART WAYS, COMMANDER.

THANK YOU FOR ALL YOUR HELP, LONI.

YES, THANK YOU!

HEY, YOU HAVEN'T GOTTEN RID OF US YET!

WE'LL SEE YOU AGAIN SOON. HAVE A SAFE FLIGHT.

FLIGHT?

NAVIN!!

MOM!

I'M SO GLAD YOU'RE SAFE.

IS EMILY WITH YOU?

NO. SHE'S WITH THE OTHER STONEKEEPERS.

I SAW THE FIREBIRD. IT WAS EMILY, WASN'T IT?

YES.

DID GABILAN SABOTAGE YOU?

NO. HE SAVED MY LIFE.

IT WAS MY FAULT. I FAILED EMILY.

SHE SAVED ME WHEN I WAS IN TROUBLE.

AND I COULDN'T DO THE SAME FOR HER.

STONEKEEPER, I AM SO PLEASED TO HAVE YOU BY MY SIDE.

DON'T TAKE THIS PERSONALLY.

MY MASTERS HAVE A GREAT DEAL OF RESPECT FOR THE PEOPLE OF ALLEDIA.

EVERYONE IS AFTER THE SAME THING, AFTER ALL.

WE ALL JUST WANT A PLACE TO CALL HOME.

OKAY, SPACE CADETS! LET'S GET THIS SHOW ON THE ROAD!

NAVIN! I NEVER SIGNED UP FOR THIS!

ON MY COUNT--

WE'RE GOING TO BE OKAY, MOM!

TEN--

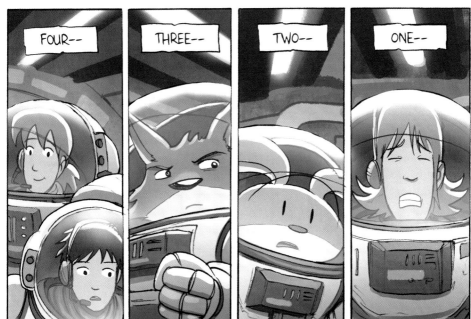

TO BE CONTINUED...

CREATED AT

BOLT CITY
PRODUCTIONS

WRITTEN & ILLUSTRATED BY
KAZU KIBUISHI

COLORS & BACKGROUNDS
JASON CAFFOE

COLOR ASSISTS
CHRYSTIN GARLAND
KAZU KIBUISHI

PAGE FLATTING
CRYSTAL KAN
MEGAN BRENNAN
NOLEN LEE

SPECIAL THANKS

Amy & Juni & Sophie Kim Kibuishi, Rachel Ormiston, Nancy Caffoe, Judy Hansen, Cassandra Pelham, David Saylor, Phil Falco, Ben Zhu & the Gallery Nucleus crew, Tao & Taka & Tyler Kibuishi, Tim Ganter, Sunni Kim, June & Masa & Julie & Emi Kibuishi, Sheila Marie Everett, Lizette Serrano, Bess Braswell, Whitney Steller, Lori Benton, and Ellie Berger.

And the biggest thanks of all to the librarians, booksellers, parents, and readers who have supported us all this way. You mean the world to us.

About the Author

Kazu Kibuishi is the creator of the #1 *New York Times* bestselling Amulet series. *Amulet, Book One: The Stonekeeper* was an ALA Best Book for Young Adults and a Children's Choice Book Award finalist. He is also the creator of *Copper*, a collection of his popular webcomic that features an adventuresome boy-and-dog pair. Kazu also illustrated the covers of the 15th anniversary paperback editions of the Harry Potter series written by J. K. Rowling. He lives and works in Seattle, Washington, with his wife, Amy Kim Kibuishi, and their children.

Visit Kazu online at www.boltcity.com.

GULFEN
GANON'S GATE
Stengard
Valcor
Skyway
Frontera
Sparkton
Lucien
Golbez
Cycle
PIT ROCK
Junivale
The Spires
Selina's
station
Vigo's Enclave
Coco
Ippo

ALSO BY KAZU KIBUISHI

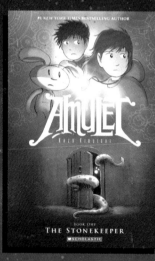

BOOK ONE
THE STONEKEEPER

BOOK TWO
THE STONEKEEPER'S CURSE

BOOK THREE
THE CLOUD SEARCHERS

BOOK FOUR
THE LAST COUNCIL

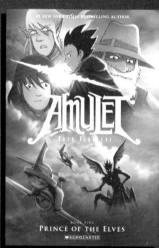

BOOK FIVE
PRINCE OF THE ELVES

BOOK SIX
ESCAPE FROM LUCIEN